Where's Santa's Elf?

To Margit, Daniella, Lucia and Skye.

Published in the UK by Scholastic Children's Books, 2020
Euston House, 24 Eversholt Street, London, NW1 1DB
A division of Scholastic Limited

London – New York – Toronto – Sydney - Auckland
Mexico City – New Delhi – Hong Kong

SCHOLASTIC and associated logos are trademarks and/or
registered trademarks of Scholastic Inc.

First published in Australia by Scholastic Australia, 2020
Text and illustrations © Bill Hope, 2020

The right of Author name and Illustrator name to be identified
as the author and illustrator of this work has been asserted by them under the Copyright,
Designs and Patents Act 1988.

ISBN 978 07023 0643 3

A CIP catalogue record for this book is available from the British Library.

Papers used by Scholastic Children's Books are made from wood grown in sustainable forests.

1 3 5 7 9 10 8 6 4 2

www.scholastic.co.uk

Bill Hope

Where's Santa's Elf?

A Scholastic Book

Dear Henry,

Congratulations! You have been accepted as a Present Fulfillment Officer at North Pole Festivities Incorporated. Your job is to collect the perfect Christmas presents for a girl named Stella.

Please report to Headquarters where we will take you through her Christmas wish list. Remember, with only two days until Christmas, Santa is counting on you!

Yours sincerely,
Esmerelda Sparkles
Head of Present Fulfillment and Delivery

STELLA McCOY 6 YRS OLD

LIKES
• UNICORNS
• GUMMY BEARS
• BEANIES

DISLIKES
• SPIDERS
• EGGS
• COFFEE

ADDRESS-
6 CHIPPING ST
HOOPERFIELD

Can you find?

Henry the Elf

Henry is an ambitious young elf out to make a splash on his first day at work. He's got a long list of presents to find for Stella, and not a lot of time to do it!

Give Henry a hand by finding him and the right present on each page!

Mrs Claus

She's the brains behind the operation. While Santa has a busy 24 hours ahead, Mrs Claus has been preparing for this day all year! As CEO of North Pole Festivities Incorporated, Mrs Claus has been organising and training hundreds of elves around the clock. Now she's finally having a rest to see her master plan come to life.

The Ghost of Christmas Present

The Ghost of Christmas Present is a friendly ghost who just wants to help out. But he's not very good. He's been trying to place this one present in the right stocking for 15 years! If you see him, try and point him in the right direction.

Prezzie

Prezzie is the spirit of excitement. She's just thrilled that Christmas is finally here and now she can see what everybody will get! You'll find her bounding all across the North Pole, spreading light and goodwill.

Santa's Sack

Sackarias Oswald O'Connor the Third, or Sack for short, used to work for Santa but developed a taste for presents and couldn't stop eating them! He's been let go now, but still lurks about trying to find one more tasty morsel. Watch your presents!

Sherbet Shepherd

The Sherbet Shepherd tends the many flocks of lollies that graze on the hillsides of the North Pole. You can always spot him with his loyal Sherbet Sheep. He's a kind fellow and always has sweets to share, so keep an eye out for him!

Baby Ru

Baby Ru has only been at the North Pole for two years, but she has already started to see how some things could change around here. That glint in her eye might be morning dew or it could be a passionate desire to win! See if you can spot her around before she becomes the next big thing!

Ol' Hasty Tasty

Ol' Hasty Tasty came out of the oven a long, long time ago. One day he tried nibbling on one of his hands and realised he was delicious! Now he's terrified that someone might try and eat him! He's been on the run ever since. See if you can catch him!

THE TOY FACTORY

Henry begins his search at the heart of the North Pole operation, The Toy Factory! Here, elves are working around the clock to have all the toys ready in time to be flown all over the world.
But all Henry needs to do is find the Rainbow Skipping Rope Stella has been wishing for . . .

Can you find?

×1 RAINBOW SKIPPING ROPE

And if you have the time . . .

2× YO-YOs

3× DUCKIES

4× MAGNIFYING GLASSES

5× SAWS

6× PAIRS OF GLASSES

7× SPANNERS

8× BEACH BALLS

9× COGS

10× TEDDY BEARS

THE CANDY CAVE

The North Pole's vast supplies of candy are guarded by the ferocious dragon, Glucagon. Henry and the other elves have to be very sneaky to collect as much candy as possible without disturbing his slumber.
Stella's favourite sweet is the mega gummy bear. There must be one hidden away in here . . .

Can you find?

×1 MEGA GUMMY BEAR

And if you have the time . . .

- **2×** OWLS
- **3×** ICE BLOCKS
- **4×** MARSH-FELLOWS
- **5×** CRACKERS
- **6×** GEMS
- **7×** KEYS
- **8×** RATS
- **9×** CANDY POPS
- **10×** BATS

KITCHEN CHAOS

It's a cacophony of culinary creation down in the Christmas kitchens. The elf chefs are hard at work getting all the gingerbread people ready for Christmas.

Stella loves all different kinds of gingerbread, but Henry thinks he can find an extra-special crunchy creature for this year . . .

Can you find?

×1 GINGER-BREAD UNICORN

And if you have the time . . .

- **2×** LADLES
- **3×** SPATULAS
- **4×** HOLLY
- **5×** MITTS
- **6×** RADISHES
- **7×** SALT SHAKERS
- **8×** TEAPOTS
- **9×** CROWNS
- **10×** PIGEONS

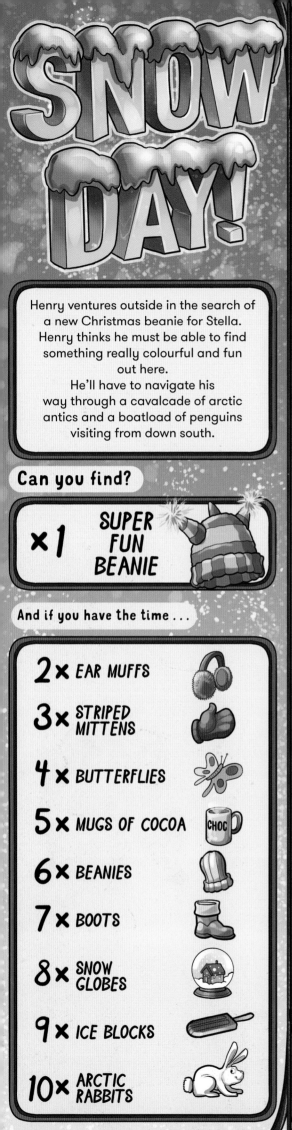

SNOW DAY!

Henry ventures outside in the search of a new Christmas beanie for Stella. Henry thinks he must be able to find something really colourful and fun out here.
He'll have to navigate his way through a cavalcade of arctic antics and a boatload of penguins visiting from down south.

Can you find?

×1 SUPER FUN BEANIE

And if you have the time . . .

2× EAR MUFFS

3× STRIPED MITTENS

4× BUTTERFLIES

5× MUGS OF COCOA

6× BEANIES

7× BOOTS

8× SNOW GLOBES

9× ICE BLOCKS

10× ARCTIC RABBITS

DECORATIONS GALORE!

What is Christmas without a flurry of festive decorations?
As the elves of the North Pole get prepared for the big day, Henry is on the search for a very particular bauble.
There must be one hidden away with Stella's name on it!
Maybe there's one with your name too!

Can you find?

×1 STELLA'S NAME BAUBLE

And if you have the time...

- **2×** ANGELS
- **3×** PENCILS
- **4×** STOCKINGS
- **5×** SCISSORS
- **6×** APPLES
- **7×** SNOWFLAKES
- **8×** DUCKIES
- **9×** MUGS
- **10×** BELLS

WRAPPER'S DELIGHT

Before millions of wonderful presents go out into the world, they'll need some wrapping! An army of elves has been working around the clock with scissors and sticky tape to make each gift a super surprise. Henry knows Stella loves polka dots, so he's on the search for a particular spotty design.
Can you help him find it?

Can you find?

×1 SPECIAL SPOTTY WRAP

And if you have the time...

2× MICE

3× ROLLS OF TAPE

4× SCISSORS

5× ROLLS OF STRING

6× GLUE

7× LABELS

8× PENCILS

9× BELLS

10× PAPER PLANES

WRAP BATTLE

ELF VILLAGE

It's almost midnight and Henry decides to stop by the Elf Village to have dinner with his family before his big journey begins. All the elves are very excited for Christmas and are celebrating in the town square. Henry is looking forward to his mum's famous mince pies and thinks Stella might like one, too.

Can you find?

×1 MUM'S MINCE PIE

And if you have the time . . .

2× TRUMPETS

3× FAIRIES

4× ROLLER SKATES

5× BUNNIES

6× BIRDIES

7× FISHIES

8× CANDLE STICKS

9× STARS

10× BELLS

SLEIGH STATIONS!

All hands on deck! The halls of the North Pole have been busy in preparation all year, but now it's go-time. While the elves pack the presents and fuel the sleigh, our team of reindeer get themselves in optimum physical condition for the night ahead. But just at the last minute, Henry has lost Stella's stocking!
Quick! Let's find it before it's too late!

Can you find?

×1 STELLA'S LOST STOCKING

And if you have the time...

- **2×** SNEAKERS
- **3×** DUMBBELLS
- **4×** PENCILS
- **5×** DRINKS
- **6×** BANANAS
- **7×** POGO STICKS
- **8×** SPANNERS
- **9×** PAINT BRUSHES
- **10×** SMOOTHIES

CHRISTMAS EVE!

The big night has arrived! Santa swoops through on his magnificent sleigh as an army of elves help deliver all the presents. They've got a big job to do and they'll need to stay out of sight. Henry's got all of Stella's presents ready to go, but now he's forgotten her address!
Although he can remember a particular pattern on her chimney.
Can you help him find it?

Can you find?

×1 CHIMNEY AT STELLA'S HOUSE!

And if you have the time . . .

2× COOKIES AND MILK

3× SKATEBOARDS

4× HOLLY

5× PHONES

6× ROLLER SKATES

7× MITTENS

8× DONUTS

9× CANDLE STICKS

10× BEANIES